Which Would You Rather Be?

By William Steig

Pictures by Harry Bliss

JOANNA COTLER BOOKS *An Imprint of HarperCollins Publishers*

This 2009 edition licensed for publication by Barnes & Noble Publishing,
Inc., by arrangement with HarperCollins Publishers.

Barnes & Noble Publishing, Inc.
122 Fifth Avenue
New York, NY 10011

ISBN 10: 1-4351-1671-2
ISBN 13: 978-1-4351-1671-9

Manufactured in China

09 10 11 12 13 SCP 10 09 08 07 06 05 04 03 02

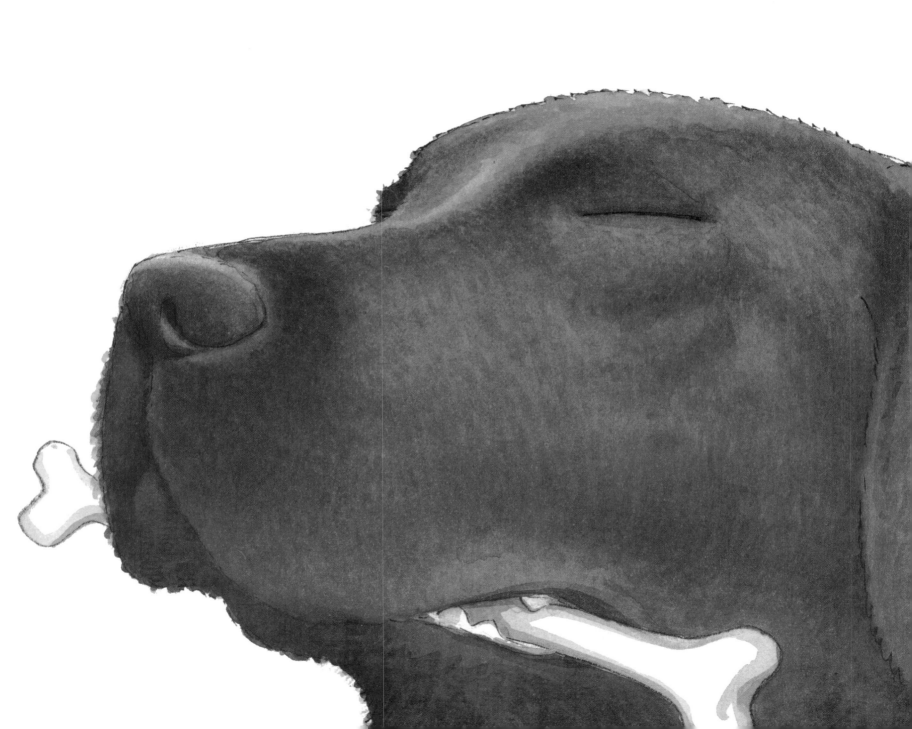

Which would you rather be?

A duck or a fox?   A flute or a tuba?

A shirt or pants?

Tall or short?

Candy or cake?

A cherry or a plum?

A moon or a sun?

Asleep or awake?